KT Tunstall
Chord Songbook
Eye to the Telescope

WISE PUBLICATIONS
part of The Music Sales Group
London / New York / Paris / Sydney / Copenhagen / Berlin / Madrid / Tokyo

Published by
Wise Publications,
8/9 Frith Street, London, W1D 3JB, England.

Exclusive distributors:
Music Sales Limited,
Distribution Centre, Newmarket Road, Bury St Edmunds,
Suffolk, IP33 3YB, England.

Music Sales Pty Limited,
120 Rothschild Avenue, Rosebery,
NSW 2018, Australia.

Order No. AM985578
ISBN 1-84609-563-8
This book © Copyright 2006 by Wise Publications,
a division of Music Sales Limited.

Music arranged by Matt Parsons, David Weston & Martin Shellard.
Music processed by Paul Ewers Music Design.
Edited by David Weston.

Printed in the United Kingdom.

www.musicsales.com

Other Side Of The World

Words & Music by
KT Tunstall & Martin Terefe

Intro

‖: D   Dsus2 | Dsus4   Dsus2 :‖

Verse 1

A   Em7
Over the sea and far a - way

                          A
She's waiting like an iceberg,

        Em7
Waiting to change.

                    A
But she's cold in - side,

                Em7   D Dsus2   Dsus4   Dsus2
She wants to be like the water.

Verse 2

A   Em7   A
All the muscles tight - en in her face,

        Em7   A
Buries her soul in one em - brace.

                    Em7
They're one and the same,

Just like water.

Chorus 1

D   Bm7
The fire fades a - way

          G
Most of everyday

        D/F♯   Em
Is full of tired excu - ses,

     A   D
But it's too hard to say.

           Bm7
I wish it were sim - ple

              G
But we give up easi - ly.

      D/F♯   Em   A   Asus4
You're close e - nough to see that

Bm   Asus4   G   A   Asus4
You're on   the oth - er side of the world to me.

| D   Dsus2 | Dsus4   Dsus2 ‖

Verse 3

A   Em7
On comes the panic light,

           A   Em7
Holding on with fingers and feelings a - like.

           A
But the time has come

   G
To move along.

Chorus 2

D   Bm7
The fire fades a - way

          G
Most of every - day

        D/F♯   Em
Is full of tired excu - ses,

     A   D
But it's too hard to say.

           Bm7
I wish it were sim - ple

              G
But we give up easi - ly.

      D/F♯   Em   A   Asus4
You're close e - nough to see that

Bm   Asus4   G   A
You're on   the other   side of the world.

Bridge

Em
Can you help me?

Gm
Can you let me go?

| **D**   **Dsus2** | **Dsus4**   **Dsus2** ‖

Em   **Bm**
And can you still love me

            A   **A/G**   **A/F♯**   **A/E**
When you can't see me anymore?

Chorus 3

        D   **Bm7**
And the fire fades a - way

                G
Most of every - day

         D/F♯   **Em**
Is full of tired excu - ses,

        A   **D**
But it's too hard to say.

               Bm7
I wish it were sim - ple

                  G
But we give up easi - ly.

         D/F♯   **Em**   **A**   **Asus4**
You're close e - nough to see that

Bm   **Asus4**   **G**   **A**
You're on   the other   side of the world.

Bm   **Asus4**   **G**   **A**
You're on   the other   side of the world.

Bm   **Asus4**   **G**   **A**   **D**
You're on   the other   side of the world to me.

Another Place To Fall

Words & Music by
KT Tunstall

Em   F   B7   G   D   Asus4   Am7   Bm7

Intro | Em | F | Em | F B7 ‖

Verse 1
          Em
Are you blind?
                   F
Blind to me trying to be kind.
                      Em
Volunteering for your firing line.
                  F   **B7**
Waiting for one precious sign.
             Em
The flicker of a smile,
                      F
You should try it just once in a while.
               Em
Baby it's not quite your style,
             F
It's simply too easy to do,
      B7   **Em**   **F**
And you might not see it through.
        Em
See it through.
F   **B7**
   Oh - oh, so

Chorus 1

```
Em  G      D   Asus⁴              Em  G  D  Asus⁴
Find your - self another place to fall.
```

```
Em  G      D                Asus⁴        Em  G  D  Asus⁴
Find your - self up against another brick wall.
```

```
Em  G      D        Asus⁴       Em  G  D  Asus⁴
See  your - self as a fallen angel.
```

```
        Em              G                      D
Well I don't see no holes in the road but you.
```

```
        Asus⁴          Em  G  D  Asus⁴
Find another place to fall.
```

Verse 2

```
              Em
Are you proud
```

```
                                    F
To have founded a brand new be - haviour
```

```
                              Em
With hatred and hurt as to your saviour.
```

```
                          F
But nobody's choosing to follow
```

```
B⁷                              Em
So you choke back the tears and you swallow.
```

```
                        F
Men who have ruined your life,
```

```
                              Em
You consume them with minimum strife.
```

```
                              F
But now you have got indi - gestion,
```

```
        B⁷                Em
The antacid comes as a question.
```

```
F       B⁷
   Oh  oh, so
```

Chorus 2

```
Em  G      D   Asus⁴              Em  G  D  Asus⁴
Find your - self another place to fall.
```

```
Em  G      D                Asus⁴        Em  G  D  Asus⁴
Find your - self up against another brick wall.
```

```
Em  G      D        Asus⁴       Em  G  D  Asus⁴
See  your - self as a fallen angel.
```

```
        Em              G                      D
Well, I don't see no holes in the road but you.
```

```
        Asus⁴          Em  G  D  Asus⁴
Find another place to fall.
```

Bridge

Am⁷   **Bm⁷**
There isn't much more I can say,

         Am⁷
For I don't understand the de - lay.

        Bm⁷
You're asking for friendly ad - vice

        Am⁷
And remaining in a permanent crisis.

      Bm⁷
Affection is yours if you ask.

        Am⁷
But first you must take off your mask.

          B⁷
When you're back's turned I've de - cided

         Em
You'll throw it away just like I did.

Am⁷ B⁷
Oh oh, so

Chorus 3

Em G **D Asus⁴**   **Em G D Asus⁴**
Find your - self another place to fall.

Em G **D**   **Asus⁴** **Em G D Asus⁴**
Find your - self up against another brick wall.

Em G **D** **Asus⁴** **Em G D Asus⁴**
See your - self as a fallen angel.

   Em   **G**   **D**
Well, I don't see no holes in the road but you.

  Asus⁴   **Em G D Asus⁴**
Find another place to fall.

Outro

   Em   **G**   **D**
‖: Well, I don't see no holes in the road but you

  Asus⁴   **Em G D Asus⁴**
Find another place to fall.   :‖ *Repeat to fade*

Under The Weather

Words & Music by
Tommy D & KT Tunstall

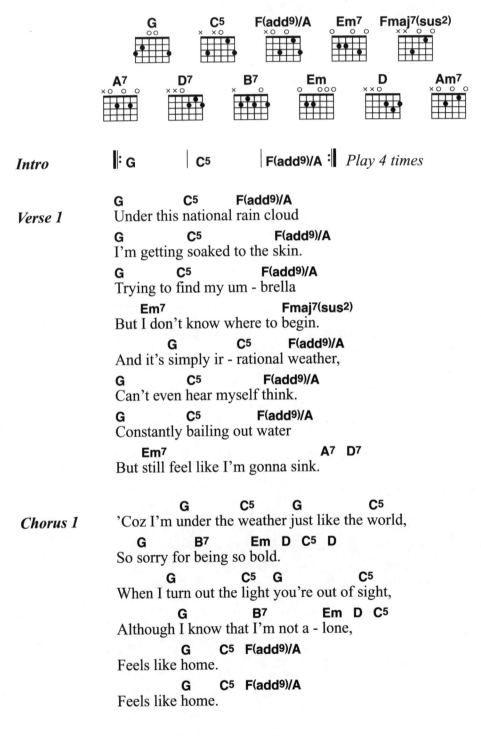

Intro ‖: G | C5 | F(add9)/A :‖ *Play 4 times*

Verse 1

G   C5   F(add9)/A
Under this national rain cloud

G   C5   F(add9)/A
I'm getting soaked to the skin.

G   C5   F(add9)/A
Trying to find my um - brella

   Em7   Fmaj7(sus2)
But I don't know where to begin.

        G   C5   F(add9)/A
And it's simply ir - rational weather,

G   C5   F(add9)/A
Can't even hear myself think.

G   C5   F(add9)/A
Constantly bailing out water

   Em7   A7   D7
But still feel like I'm gonna sink.

Chorus 1

        G   C5   G   C5
'Coz I'm under the weather just like the world,

    G   B7   Em D C5 D
So sorry for being so bold.

        G   C5   G   C5
When I turn out the light you're out of sight,

        G   B7   Em D C5
Although I know that I'm not a - lone,

        G   C5 F(add9)/A
Feels like home.

        G   C5 F(add9)/A
Feels like home.

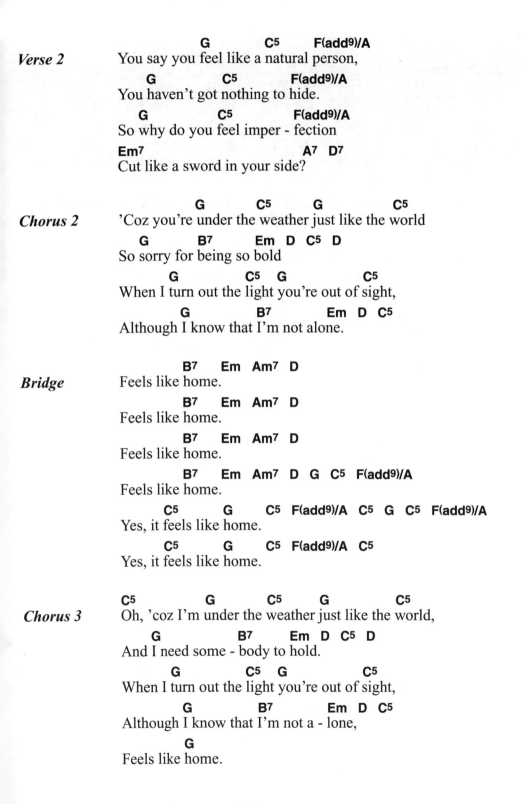

Verse 2

           G   **C5**   **F(add9)/A**
You say you feel like a natural person,

       G   **C5**   **F(add9)/A**
You haven't got nothing to hide.

        G   **C5**   **F(add9)/A**
So why do you feel imper - fection

Em7   **A7** **D7**
Cut like a sword in your side?

Chorus 2

           G   **C5**   **G**   **C5**
'Coz you're under the weather just like the world

       G   **B7**   **Em** **D** **C5** **D**
So sorry for being so bold

        G   **C5** **G**   **C5**
When I turn out the light you're out of sight,

          G   **B7**   **Em** **D** **C5**
Although I know that I'm not alone.

Bridge

         B7   **Em** **Am7** **D**
Feels like home.

         B7   **Em** **Am7** **D**
Feels like home.

         B7   **Em** **Am7** **D**
Feels like home.

         B7   **Em** **Am7** **D** **G** **C5** **F(add9)/A**
Feels like home.

      C5   **G**   **C5** **F(add9)/A** **C5** **G** **C5** **F(add9)/A**
Yes, it feels like home.

      C5   **G**   **C5** **F(add9)/A** **C5**
Yes, it feels like home.

Chorus 3

C5   **G**   **C5**   **G**   **C5**
Oh, 'coz I'm under the weather just like the world,

    G   **B7**   **Em** **D** **C5** **D**
And I need some - body to hold.

       G   **C5** **G**   **C5**
When I turn out the light you're out of sight,

        G   **B7**   **Em** **D** **C5**
Although I know that I'm not a - lone,

       G
Feels like home.

Suddenly I See

Words & Music by
KT Tunstall

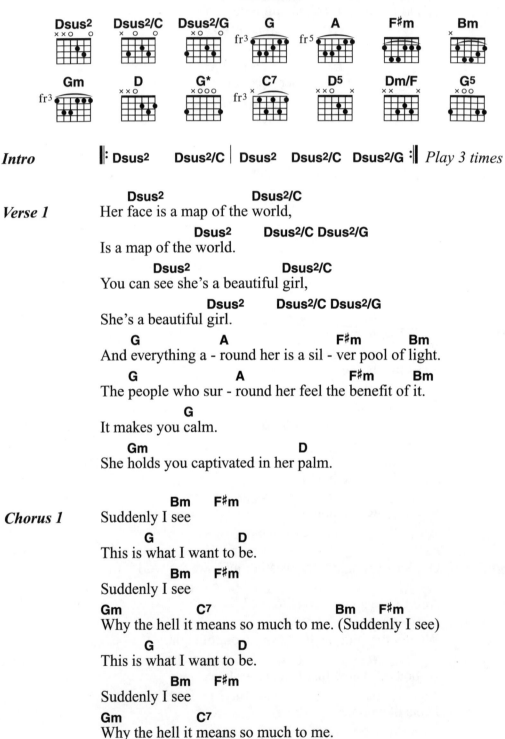

Intro   ‖: Dsus2   Dsus2/C │ Dsus2   Dsus2/C   Dsus2/G :‖ *Play 3 times*

Verse 1

      Dsus2   Dsus2/C
Her face is a map of the world,

           Dsus2   Dsus2/C Dsus2/G
Is a map of the world.

       Dsus2   Dsus2/C
You can see she's a beautiful girl,

           Dsus2   Dsus2/C Dsus2/G
She's a beautiful girl.

    G   A   F♯m   Bm
And everything a - round her is a sil - ver pool of light.

    G   A   F♯m   Bm
The people who sur - round her feel the benefit of it.

           G
It makes you calm.

    Gm   D
She holds you captivated in her palm.

Chorus 1

       Bm   F♯m
Suddenly I see

    G   D
This is what I want to be.

       Bm   F♯m
Suddenly I see

Gm   C7   Bm   F♯m
Why the hell it means so much to me. (Suddenly I see)

    G   D
This is what I want to be.

       Bm   F♯m
Suddenly I see

Gm   C7
Why the hell it means so much to me.

Instrumental ‖: **Dsus2**   **Dsus2/C** | **Dsus2**   **Dsus2/C**   **Dsus2/G** :‖

          Dsus2   **Dsus2/C**

Verse 2   I feel like walking the world,

                     Dsus2   **Dsus2/C Dsus2/G**

     Like walking the   world.

             Dsus2   **Dsus2/C**

     You can hear she's a beautiful girl,

                 Dsus2   **Dsus2/C Dsus2/G**

     She's a beautiful girl.

        G   **A**   **F♯m**   **Bm**

     She fills up every corner like she's born in black and white.

     G   **A**   **F♯m**   **Bm**

     Makes you feel warmer when you're trying to re - member

             G

     What you heard.

      Gm   **D**

     She likes to leave you hanging on a word.

                 Bm   **F♯m**

Chorus 2   Suddenly I see

           G   **D**

     This is what I want to be.

                 Bm   **F♯m**

     Suddenly I see

     Gm   **C7**   **Bm**   **F♯m**

     Why the hell it means so much to me. (Suddenly I see)

           G   **D**

     This is what I want to be.

                 Bm   **F♯m**

     Suddenly I see

     Gm   **C7**   **D5**

     Why the hell it means so much to me.

               Dm/F   **D5**

Bridge   And she's taller than most

               Dm/F   **D5/G**

     And she's looking at me.

     D5   **Dm/F**   **D5**   **Dm/F D5/G**

     I can see her eyes looking from a page in a maga - zine.

     D5   **Dm/F**   **D5**

     Oh she makes me feel like I could be a tower.

      Dm/F   **G5**

     A big strong tower, yeah.

     D5

     The power to be,

cont.

Dm/F
The power to give,

D5
The power to see, yeah yeah.

    Dm/F   **D5/G**   **Dsus2**
𝄆 (Sudden - ly I see.) She got the power to be,

     Dsus2/C   **Dsus2**
The power to give, the power to see, yeah yeah.

Dsus2/C **Dsus2/G** **Dsus2**
(Suddenly I see.)   She got the power to be,

     Dsus2/C   **Dsus2**
The power to give, the power to see, yeah yeah. 𝄇

Chorus 3

  D5   **Dm/F** **Bm** **F♯m**
Sudden - ly I— see

     G   **D**
This is what I want to be,

     Bm   **F♯m**
Suddenly I see

Gm   **C7**   **Bm**   **F♯m**
Why the hell it means so much to me. (Suddenly I see)

       G   **D**
This is what I want to be.

     Bm   **F♯m**
Suddenly I see (Suddenly I see)

Gm   **C7**   **D5**
Why the hell it means so much to me.

Bm **F♯m**   **G**   **D**
Oh yeah
(Suddenly I see)

Bm   **F♯m**
Suddenly I see

Gm   **C7**
Why the hell it means so much to me.

Bm **F♯m** **G**
Yeah, yeah
(Suddenly I see)

D   **Bm**   **F♯m**
Suddenly I see

Gm   **C7**   **D**
Why the hell it means so much to me.

Miniature Disasters

Words & Music by
KT Tunstall

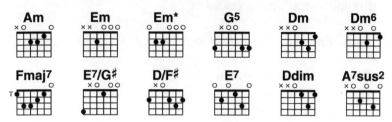

Intro riff   ‖: Am Em Am Em* G5 :‖ *Play 4 times*

Verse 1

N.C   Am Em Am
I don't want to be se - cond best,

Em*   G5   Am Em Am
  Don't want to stand in   line.

Em*   G5   Am Em Am
  Don't want to fall be - hind.

Em* G5 Am Em Am

Am   Dm
  Don't want to get caught out,

            Dm6
Don't want to do without.

| Am Em Am Em* G5 | Am Em Am |
            Fmaj7   G5
Oh and the lesson I must learn

            E7/G#
Is that I've got to wait my turn.

Link 1   ‖: Am Em Am Em* G5 :‖ *Play 3 times*

| Am Em Am ‖

Verse 2

N.C   Am Em Am
Looks like I got to be hot and cold,

Em*   G5   Am   Em Am
  I got to be taught and told.

Em*   G5   Am   Em Am
  Got to be good as   gold.

Em* G5 Am Em Am

Am   **Dm**   **Dm6**
  But perfectly honestly, oh

I think it won't be good for me.

| **Am Em Am Em* G5** | **Am Em Am** |
      Fmaj7   **G5**
'Coz it's a hindrance to my health
      E7/G♯
If I'm a stranger to myself.

| **Am Em Am Em* G5** | **Am Em Am** |

Chorus 1

D/F♯   **Am**
Miniature disasters and minor catastrophes
D/F♯   **Am Em Am Em**
Bring me to my knees.
      Fmaj7
Well I must be my own master
   G5   **Am**
Or a miniature disaster will be,
E7
  It will be the death of me.

Link 1

‖: **Am Em Am Em* G5** :‖ *Play 3 times*

| **Am Em Am** ‖

Verse 3

N.C   **Am Em Am**
I don't have to raise my voice
Em*   **G5**   **Am Em Am**
  Don't have to be un - der - hand,
Em* G5   **Am Em Am**
  Just got to un - der - stand

Em* G5 Am Em Am

Am   **Dm**
  That it's gonna be up and down,
         Dm6
It's gonna be lost and found.

| **Am Em Am Em* G5** | **Am Em Am** |
     Fmaj7   **G5**
And I can't take to the sky
      E7/G♯
Before I like it on the ground.

`| Am  Em  Am  Em*  G5 | Am  Em  Am |`

Bridge

Fmaj7
And I need to be patient

G5
And I need to be brave,

E7/G#
Need to discover

Am
How I need to behave.

Fmaj7
And I'll find out the answers

G5
When I know what to ask.

Ddim
But I speak a different language

And everybody's talking too fast.

Chorus 2

D/F#   Am
Miniature disasters and minor catastrophes

D/F#   Am Em Am Em
Bring me to my knees.

Fmaj7
Well, I must be my own master

G5   Am   D/F#
Or a miniature disaster will be,   will be, yeah, yeah.

Fmaj7
Well I've got to run a little faster

G5   Am   D/F#
Or a miniature disaster will be,   will be, oh,

Fmaj7
Well, I need to know I'll last if a little

G5   Am
Miniature disaster hits me.

E7   A7sus2
 Oh, It will be the death of me.

Silent Sea

Words & Music by
KT Tunstall & Hogarth

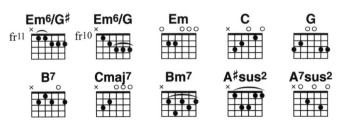

Intro ‖: Em6/G♯ | Em6/G :‖

Verse 1

      Em   **C**
I was happy in my harbour

        G   **B7**
When you cut me loose.

Em   **C**
Floating on an ocean

       G   **B7**
And con - fused.

Em   **C**
Winds are whipping waves up

       G   **B7**
Like sky scrapers.

      Em   **C**
And the harder they hit me

   G **B7**   **Em C G B7**
The less I seem to bruise.

Chorus 1

      Cmaj7
Oh when I

       Bm7
Find the con - trols

      A♯sus2
I'll go where I like,

        A7sus2 **Cmaj7**
I'll know where I want to be.

      Bm7
But maybe for now

      A♯sus2
I'll stay right here

cont.

   A7sus2 Em C G
On a silent sea.

   B7 Em C G B7
On a silent sea.

Verse 2

    Em   C
I was happy in my harbour

      G B7
When you cut me loose.

Em   C
Floating on an ocean

      G B7
And con - fused.

Link   ‖: Em | C | G | B7 :‖

Chorus 2

    Cmaj7
Oh when I

     Bm7
Find the con - trols

      A#sus2
I'll go where I like,

       A7sus2 Cmaj7
I'll know where I want to be

      Bm7
But maybe for now

      A#sus2
I'll stay right here

   A7sus2 Cmaj7 Bm7
On a silent sea.

     A#sus2 A7sus2 Cmaj7 Bm7
On a silent sea.   oh

     A#sus2
I'll stay right here

   A7sus2
On a silent sea.

Link ‖: **Em6/G♯** | **Em6/G** :‖ *Play 4 times*
Vocal ad libs.

Chorus 3

        Cmaj7
Oh when I

           Bm7
Find the con - trols

          A♯sus2
I'll go where I like,

             A7sus2 Cmaj7
I'll know where I want to be

          Bm7
But maybe for now

          A♯sus2
I'll stay right here

       A7sus2
On a silent sea.

Universe & U

Words & Music by
KT Tunstall & Pleasure

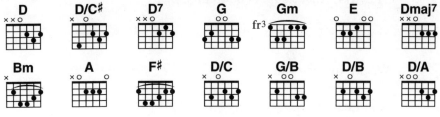

Intro | D | D/C♯ | D7 | G Gm ||

Verse 1

     D   D/C♯
    A fire burns,

              D7
Water comes.

             G   Gm
You cool me down,

                 D
When I'm cold in - side

              E
You are warm and bright.

                 G
You know you are so good for me, yeah.

D   Dmaj7
  With your child's eyes

                D7
You are more than you seem.

           G
You see into space.

           Gm
I see in your face

              D
The places you've been,

             E
The things you have learned.

             G
They sit with you so beautifully, yeah

Chorus 1

Bm   A
You know there's no need to hide away.

                    G
You know I tell the truth.

              D
We are just the same.

     Bm   A
And I can feel every - thing you do,

                F♯
Hear everything   you say,

                   G
Even when you're miles away.

             Gm   D
'Coz I am me, the universe and you.

Link 1 | D | D/C♯ | D7 | G/B ‖

Bridge

     Gm   D
And just like stars burning bright,

                  E
Making holes in the night,

              G
We are building bridges.

Chorus 2

Bm   A
You know there's no need to hide   away.

                    G
You know I tell the   truth.

              D
We are just the same.

     Bm   A
And I can feel everything   you do,

                F♯
Hear everything you say

                   G
Even when you're miles away.

          G   Bm A
'Cause I am me, the universe and you, oh,

                            D
I'm the universe and you,   oh,

Bm   A

And when you're on your own

                      F♯

I'll send you a sign

                 G

Just so you know

Gm   D Dmaj7

I am me, the universe and you.

                      D7 G

The universe and you.

                    Gm D D/C♯ D/B D/A G

The universe and you.

                      D

I am the universe and you.

False Alarm

Words & Music by
KT Tunstall

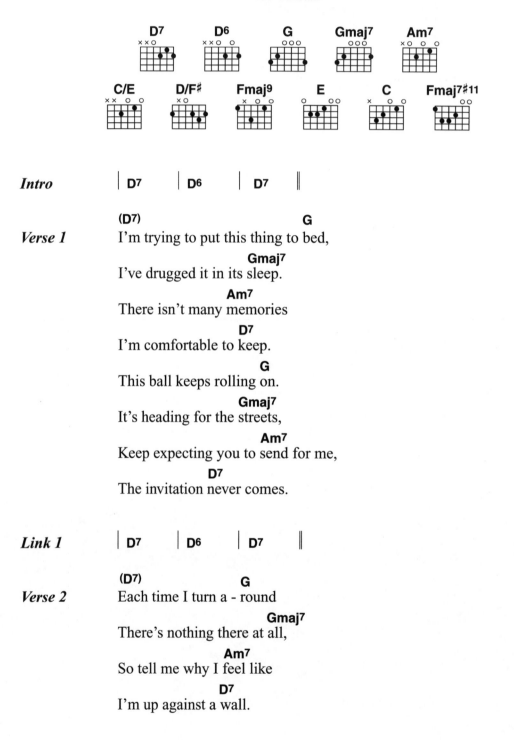

Intro | D7 | D6 | D7 ||

Verse 1

(D7)   G
I'm trying to put this thing to bed,

                          Gmaj7
I've drugged it in its sleep.

                    Am7
There isn't many memories

                    D7
I'm comfortable to keep.

                    G
This ball keeps rolling on.

                    Gmaj7
It's heading for the streets,

                          Am7
Keep expecting you to send for me,

                    D7
The invitation never comes.

Link 1 | D7 | D6 | D7 ||

Verse 2

(D7)   G
Each time I turn a - round

                              Gmaj7
There's nothing there at all,

                    Am7
So tell me why I feel like

                    D7
I'm up against a wall.

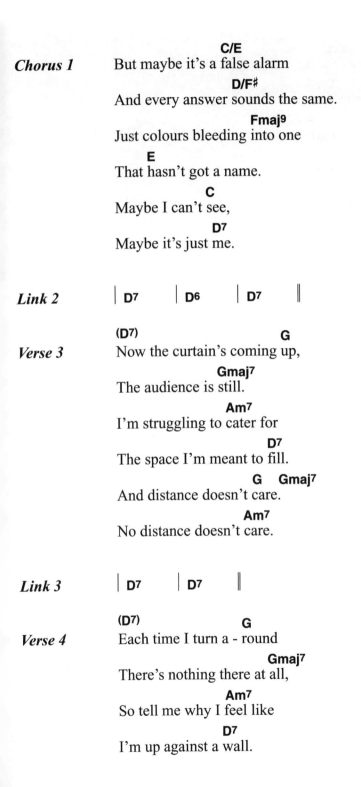

Chorus 1

                C/E
But maybe it's a false alarm
                    D/F♯
And every answer sounds the same.
                   Fmaj9
Just colours bleeding into one
        E
That hasn't got a name.
            C
Maybe I can't see,
            D7
Maybe it's just me.

Link 2

| **D7** | **D6** | **D7** | ‖

Verse 3

(D7)   **G**
Now the curtain's coming up,
               Gmaj7
The audience is still.
              Am7
I'm struggling to cater for
                  D7
The space I'm meant to fill.
                G   **Gmaj7**
And distance doesn't care.
              Am7
No distance doesn't care.

Link 3

| **D7** | **D7** | ‖

Verse 4

(D7)   **G**
Each time I turn a - round
                   Gmaj7
There's nothing there at all,
              Am7
So tell me why I feel like
              D7
I'm up against a wall.

Chorus 2

                C/E
But maybe it's a false alarm

                D/F♯
And every answer sounds the same.

                Fmaj$_{9}^{9}$
Just colours bleeding into one

       E
That hasn't got a name.

         C
Maybe I can't see,

          D$_7$
Maybe it's just me.

Link 4 | **D$_7$** | **D$_6$** | **D$_7$**   ‖

       (D$_7$)   **G**
Outro   I'm trying to put this thing to bed.

               Gmaj$_7$
I drugged it in its sleep.

                Am$_7$
Remember what you said.

                 D$_7$ **D$_6$**
Are you comfortable to keep it?

D$_7$ **D$_6$**
Keep it?

    | **Fmaj$_7$♯^{11}** | **E**   ‖

Heal Over

Words & Music by
KT Tunstall

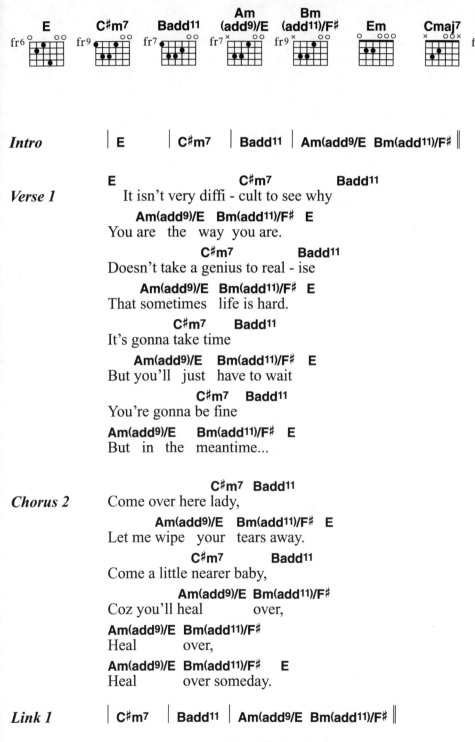

Intro
| E | C#m7 | Badd11 | Am(add9/E Bm(add11)/F# ‖

Verse 1

  E   C#m7   Badd11
    It isn't very diffi - cult to see why
       Am(add9)/E Bm(add11)/F# E
  You are the way you are.
                  C#m7   Badd11
  Doesn't take a genius to real - ise
       Am(add9)/E Bm(add11)/F# E
  That sometimes   life is hard.
              C#m7   Badd11
  It's gonna take time
       Am(add9)/E Bm(add11)/F#   E
  But you'll   just   have to wait
              C#m7   Badd11
  You're gonna be fine
  Am(add9)/E   Bm(add11)/F#   E
  But in the meantime...

Chorus 2

              C#m7 Badd11
  Come over here lady,
       Am(add9)/E Bm(add11)/F#   E
  Let me wipe   your   tears away.
              C#m7   Badd11
  Come a little nearer baby,
                Am(add9)/E Bm(add11)/F#
  Coz you'll heal   over,
  Am(add9)/E Bm(add11)/F#
  Heal   over,
  Am(add9)/E Bm(add11)/F#   E
  Heal   over someday.

Link 1
| C#m7 | Badd11 | Am(add9/E Bm(add11)/F# ‖

Verse 2

    E   C#m7   Badd11
And I don't wanna hear you tell your - self

             Am(add9)/E   Bm(add11)/F#   E
That these feelings are in the past.

                        C#m7   Badd11
You know it doesn't mean they're off the shelf

             Am(add9)/E   Bm(add11)/F#   E
Because pain's built to last.

           C#m7   Badd11
Everybody sails alone.

           Am(add9)/E   Bm(add11)/F#   E
Oh, but we   can   travel side by side.

            C#m7   Badd11
Even if you fail

              Am(add9)/E   Bm(add11)/F#   E
You know that no one really minds.

Chorus 2   As Chorus 1

Link 2   ‖: Em | Cmaj7 Gmaj7/D :‖

Middle

    Em   Cmaj7 Gmaj7/D   Em
And don't hold on but don't let go.

          Cmaj7 Gmaj7/D
I know it's so hard.

   Em   Cmaj7   Gmaj7/D   Em
   You've got to try to trust your - self,

          Cmaj7 Gmaj7/D   Cmaj7
I know it's so hard. So hard. Yeah.

Chorus 3

    E   C#m7   Badd11
Come over here lady,

         Am(add9)/E Bm(add11)/F#   E
Let me wipe   your   tears away.

           C#m7   Badd11
Come a little nearer baby,

         Am(add9)/E   Bm(add11)/F#
Coz you'll heal   over,

Am(add9)/E Bm(add11)/F#
Heal   over,

Am(add9)/E Bm(add11)/F# E C#m7   Badd11
Heal   over someday.

         Am(add9)/E Bm(add11)/F#   E
Yeah, you're gonna   heal over.

Stoppin' The Love

Words & Music by
Tommy D & KT Tunstall

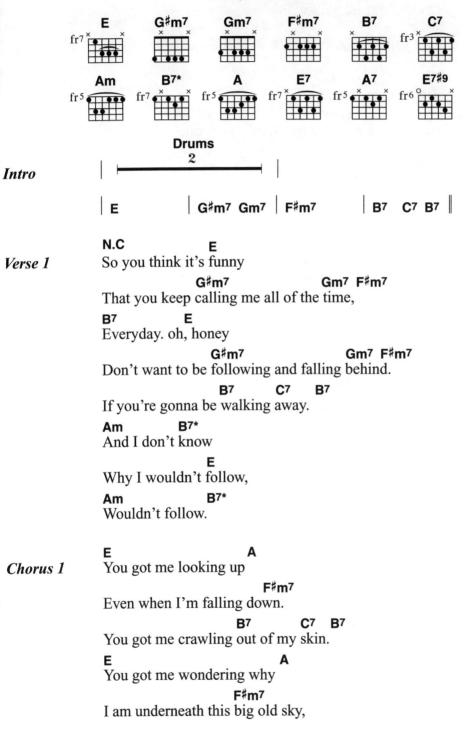

Intro

| E | G♯m7 Gm7 | F♯m7 | B7 C7 B7 ‖

Verse 1

N.C   E
So you think it's funny

      G♯m7   Gm7   F♯m7
That you keep calling me all of the time,

B7   E
Everyday. oh, honey

      G♯m7   Gm7   F♯m7
Don't want to be following and falling behind.

      B7   C7   B7
If you're gonna be walking away.

Am   B7*
And I don't know

           E
Why I wouldn't follow,

Am   B7*
Wouldn't follow.

Chorus 1

E   A
You got me looking up

         F♯m7
Even when I'm falling down.

      B7   C7   B7
You got me crawling out of my skin.

E   A
You got me wondering why

        F♯m7
I am underneath this big old sky,

cont.

C7   B7   E7 | A7
Stopping the loving getting in.

E7   A7
But I'm stopping the loving getting in.

Verse 2

N.C   E
Now you say it's easy

          G#m7   Gm7 F#m7
That you been falling for all of my charm,

       B7   E
And getting lost in my smile.

         G#m7   Gm7
Never ceases to amaze me

                F#m7
When I'm chancing my arm

       B7 C7 B7
That I still do it with style.

Am
And now I hope

B7*   E
You'll be with me to - morrow,

    Am   B7*
With me tomorrow.

Chorus 2

E   A
You got me looking up

            F#m7
Even when I'm falling down.

             B7   C7 B7
You got me crawling out of my skin.

E   A
You got me wondering why

            F#m7
I am underneath this big old sky,

C7   B7   E7 | A7
Stopping the loving getting in.

E7   A7
Stopping the loving getting in.

E7   A7
Stopping the loving getting in.

Instrumental   ‖: **E7** | **A7**   :‖
              Vocals ad lib.

E   **A**

Chorus 3   You got me looking up

                     F♯m7

Even when I'm falling down.

                B7   **C7**   **B7**

You got me crawling out of my skin.

E   **A**

You got me wondering why

             F♯m7

I am underneath this big old sky,

C7   **B7**   **E7♯9**

Stopping the loving getting in.

Drums to fade

Through The Dark

Words & Music by
KT Tunstall & Martin Terefe

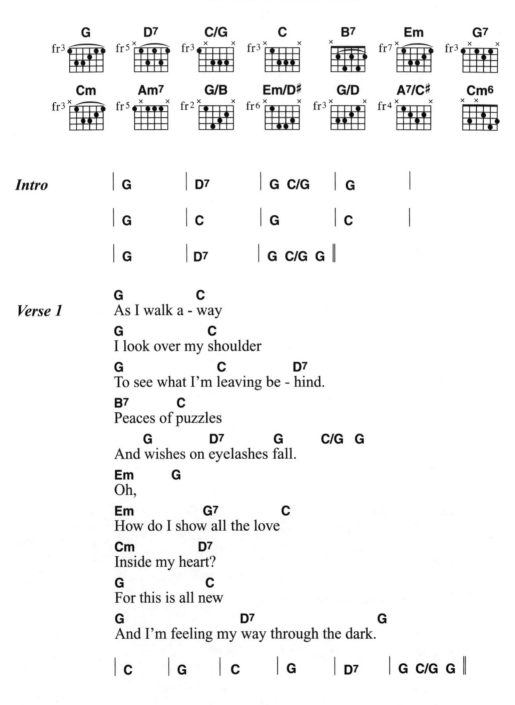

Intro

| G | D7 | G C/G | G | |

| G | C | G | C | |

| G | D7 | G C/G G ‖

Verse 1

G   C
As I walk a - way

G   C
I look over my shoulder

G   C   D7
To see what I'm leaving be - hind.

B7   C
Peaces of puzzles

      G   D7   G   C/G   G
And wishes on eyelashes fall.

Em   G
Oh,

Em   G7   C
How do I show all the love

Cm   D7
Inside my heart?

G   C
For this is all new

G   D7   G
And I'm feeling my way through the dark.

| C | G | C | G | D7 | G C/G G ‖

Verse 2

G   C
And I used to talk

      G   C
With honest convic - tion

    G   C   D7
Of how I pre - dicted my word.

         B7   C
I'm gon - na leave it to star gazers,

      G   D7   G   C/G   G
Tell me what you telescope says.

Em   G   Em   G7   C   Cm
Oh,   what is in store for me now?

             D7
It's coming a - part.

G   C
I know that it's true

G   D7   G
'Cos I'm feeling my way through the dark.

Bridge

Am7   D7
Try to find a light on somewhere.

Am7   D7
Try to find a light on somewhere.

Am7   Cm
I'm finding I'm falling in love with the dark, over here.

| G/B | G   ‖

Verse 3

Em   G   Em   G7   C   Cm
Oh, oh, what do I know? I don't care

          D7
Where I start.

        G   C
For my troubles are few

           G   D7   Em
As I'm feel - ing my way through the dark.

Em/D♯   G/D   A7/C♯
   Through the dark,

     Cm6   D7   G | Cm |
I'm feeling my way through the dark.

| G | Cm | G | D7 | G   ‖

Black Horse And The Cherry Tree

Words & Music by
KT Tunstall

Em   B7   D   D6/A   Cmaj7   C9   E7sus4

Intro

Percussion
8

N.C.
Whoo-hoo, whoo-hoo. whoo-hoo, whoo-hoo. *Play 3 times*

Em
Whoo-hoo, whoo-hoo.

Em   B7 Em
Whoo-hoo, whoo-hoo.

Verse 1

N.C.
Well my heart knows me better than I know myself

So I'm gonna let it do all the talking.
Em   B7 Em
Whoo-hoo, whoo-hoo.

N.C.
I came across a place in the middle of nowhere

With a big black horse and a cherry tree.
Em   B7 Em
Whoo-hoo, whoo-hoo.

N.C.
I felt a little fear, upon my back

I said don't look back, just keep on walking.
Em   B7 Em
Whoo-hoo, whoo-hoo

N.C.
And the big, black horse said "Hey, let's dance

Look at is this way, will you marry me?"
Em   B7 Em
Whoo-hoo, whoo-hoo.

                    Em D
But I said no, no,

D6/A Cmaj7
No,— no, no, no

            Em D
I said no, no

C9   **Em**
You're not the one for me.

      D
No, no

D6/A Cmaj7
No,— no, no, no

            Em D
I said no, no

C9
You're not the one for me.

          Em   **B7 Em**
Whoo-hoo, whoo-hoo.

          Em   **B7 Em**
Whoo-hoo, whoo-hoo.

Verse 2

     N.C.
My heart hit a problem, in the early hours

So it stopped it dead for a beat or two

          Em   **B7 Em**
Whoo-hoo, whoo-hoo.

N.C.
But I cut some cord, and I shouldn't have done it

And it won't forgive me after all these years.

          Em   **B7 Em**
Whoo-hoo, whoo-hoo.

N.C.
So I sent her to a place in the middle of nowhere

With a big black horse and a cherry tree

          Em   **B7 Em**
Whoo-hoo, whoo-hoo.

N.C.
Now it won't come back, 'cause it's oh so happy

And now I've got a hole for the world to see.

          Em   **B7 Em**
Whoo-hoo, whoo-hoo.

Chorus 2

           Em D
But it said no,   no,

D6/A   Cmaj7
No,— no, no, no

         Em D
It said no,   no

C9   **Em**
You're not the one for me.

       D
No, no,

D6/A   Cmaj7
No,— no, no, no

         Em D
It said no,   no

C9
You're not the one for me.

         Em   **B7 Em**
Whoo-hoo, whoo-hoo.

Bridge

   N.C.
‖: No, no, no, no

No, no, no, no

No, no, no, no

You're not the one for me. :‖

Interlude

N.C.
‖: Doo-doo, doo, doo, doo-be, doo

Doo-doo, be-doo :‖ *Play 4 times*

Well, there was a

‖: Big black horse and a cherry tree.

I can't quite get there coz my heart's forsaken me. Yeah. :‖

Big black horse and a cherry tree.
E⁷sus⁴   Em
Big black horse and a cherry tree.
Em   D
No,   no
Cmaj⁷   Em
No, no, no, no
         D
No, no, no, no
      Cmaj⁷   Em
My heart's forsaken me.
Em   D   Cmaj⁷   Em
Big black horse and a cherry tree.
              D   C⁹   Em
I can't quite get there 'cause my heart's forsaken me. Yeah.
Em   D   Cmaj⁷   Em
Big black horse and a cherry tree.
              D   C⁹   N.C
I can't quite get there 'cause my heart's forsaken me.

1 2 3 4 5 6 7 8 9

37

Relative Tuning

The guitar can be tuned with the aid of pitch pipes or dedicated electronic guitar tuners which are available through your local music dealer. If you do not have a tuning device, you can use relative tuning. Estimate the pitch of the 6th string as near as possible to E or at least a comfortable pitch (not too high, as you might break other strings in tuning up). Then, while checking the various positions on the diagram, place a finger from your left hand on the:

5th fret of the E or 6th string and **tune the open A** (or 5th string) to the note (A)

5th fret of the A or 5th string and **tune the open D** (or 4th string) to the note (D)

5th fret of the D or 4th string and **tune the open G** (or 3rd string) to the note (G)

4th fret of the G or 3rd string and **tune the open B** (or 2nd string) to the note (B)

5th fret of the B or 2nd string and **tune the open E** (or 1st string) to the note (E)

E	A	D	G	B	E
or	or	or	or	or	or
6th	5th	4th	3rd	2nd	1st

Head

Nut

1st Fret

2nd Fret

3rd Fret

4th Fret

5th Fret

Reading Chord Boxes

Chord boxes are diagrams of the guitar neck viewed head upwards, face on as illustrated. The top horizontal line is the nut, unless a higher fret number is indicated, the others are the frets.

The vertical lines are the strings, starting from E (or 6th) on the left to E (or 1st) on the right.

The black dots indicate where to place your fingers.

Strings marked with an O are played open, not fretted. Strings marked with an X should not be played.

The curved bracket indicates a 'barre' - hold down the strings under the bracket with your first finger, using your other fingers to fret the remaining notes.

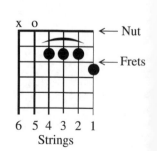

← Nut

← Frets

6 5 4 3 2 1
Strings